To

From

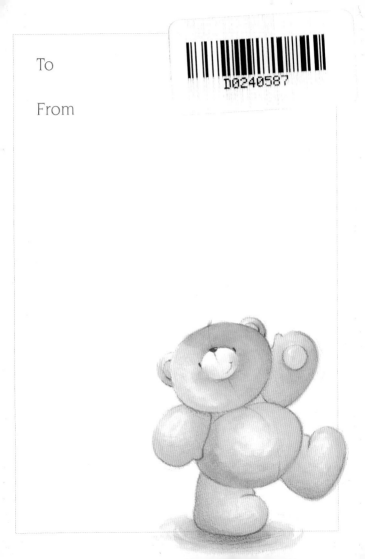

The very

best of life

Bright flowers! Beauty! Joy!
The very best of life!
That's what I wish for you.

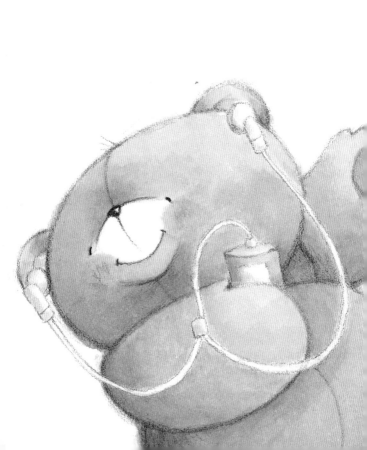

Be happy!

Listen to the music you love.
Surround yourself
with things that make you feel spoiled.
Love life! Be happy!

Friends

Find kind, gentle friends.
Find fun friends to share free,
happy days. Enjoy being with them.
May there always be friends
to share your laughter, your troubles
and your victories.

Time enough
to be reasonable and sensible
and careful.
But now - go for it! Enjoy!

Discovery.

I wish you the joy of discovery.
Of learning, of ideas,
and stretching your thoughts.

I wish you quiet sleep,
good dreams,
happy awakenings.

Travel to see the flowers in Spring!
Walk the wild moor!
Go and find the beautiful places.
I hope you'll make time
to see the world.

I love to watch you
happily working away.
Busy, busy, busy.
Planning, adding your personal touch,
just doing what you do best.

When I see you worried...
When I see you low...
That's when I wish you hope and strength
and growing happiness.

I wish you the discovery
of what you're really good at
and what you really want to do.
And that you'll have the courage
and the luck that make
dreams come true.

I like it most
when you're full of hope -
when you believe
you're the bees' knees.
Always believe it.
You're the greatest!

A life

I wish you a day filled with smiles and surprises, and a life of adventures and excitement!

Most of all I

...quiet and feeling at ease.
Taking time to just be,
without stress and hassle.
Yes, I wish you peace
and contentment.

wish you...